# Cash management

## Workbook

Aubrey Penning

Michael Fardon

osborne
BOOKS

Published by Osborne Books Limited
Unit 1B Everoak Estate
Bromyard Road
Worcester WR2 5HP
Tel 01905 748071
Email books@osbornebooks.co.uk
Website www.osbornebooks.co.uk

Design by Laura Ingham
Cover and page design image © Istockphoto.com/Petrovich9

Printed by CPI Antony Rowe Limited, Chippenham

British Library Cataloguing in Publication Data
A catalogue record for this book is available from the British Library

ISBN 978 1905777 471

# Contents

## Chapter activities

## Chapter activities – answers

## Practice assessments

## Practice assessments – answers

# Acknowledgements

The publisher wishes to thank the following for their help with the reading and production of the book: Maz Loton, Jon Moore and Cathy Turner. Thanks are also due to Jo Osborne for her technical editorial work and to Laura Ingham for her designs for this series.

The publisher is indebted to the Association of Accounting Technicians for its kind permission to reproduce sample practice assessment material.

# Authors

**Aubrey Penning** has many years experience of teaching accountancy on a variety of courses in Worcester and Gwent. He is a Certified Accountant, and before his move into full-time teaching he worked for the health service, a housing association and a chemical supplier. Until recently he was the AAT course coordinator at Worcester College of Technology, specialising in the areas of management accounting and taxation.

**Michael Fardon** has extensive teaching experience of a wide range of banking, business and accountancy courses at Worcester College of Technology. He now specialises in writing business and financial texts and is General Editor at Osborne Books. He is also an educational consultant and has worked extensively in the areas of vocational business curriculum development.

# Introduction

## what this book covers

This book has been written specifically to cover the Learning Area 'Cash Management' which combines two QCF Units in the AAT Level 3 Diploma in Accounting:

- Principles of cash management
- Cash management

## what this book contains

This book is set out in two sections:

- **Chapter activities** which provide extra practice material in addition to the activities included in the Osborne Books Tutorial text. Answers to the Chapter activities are set out in this book.
- **Practice assessments** are included to prepare the student for the Computer Based Assessments. They are based directly on the structure, style and content of the sample assessment material provided by the AAT at www.aat.org.uk. Suggested answers to the Practice assessments are set out in this book.

## online support from Osborne Books

This book is supported by practice material available at www.osbornebooks.co.uk

This material is available to tutors – and to students at their discretion – in two forms:

- A **Tutor Zone** which is available to tutors who have adopted the Osborne Books texts. This area of the website provides extra assessment practice material (plus answers) in addition to the activities included in this Workbook text.
- **E-learning** – online practice questions designed to familiarise students with the style of the AAT Computer Based Assessments.

## further information

If you want to know more about our products, please visit www.osbornebooks.co.uk, email books@osbornebooks.co.uk or telephone Osborne Books Customer Services on 01905 748071.

# Chapter activities

| 1 | **Chapter activities** |
|---|---|
|   | **Managing cash flows** |

**1.1**

**(a)** Complete the diagram below of the working capital cycle by placing the options into the correct boxes.

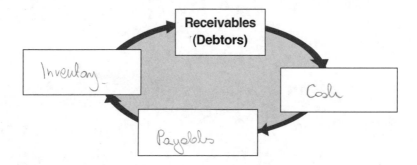

**Options:**

■ Payables (creditors)

■ Cash

■ Inventory (stock)

**(b)** A business has an average inventory (stock) holding period of 95 days; receives payment from its customers in 55 days and pays its suppliers in 80 days.

What is the cash operating cycle in days for the business? (Select one)

| | ✓ |
|---|---|
| 230 days | |
| 120 days | |
| 40 days | |
| 70 days | √ |

**1.2** Complete the following table by selecting one or more appropriate phrases for each box from the options listed.

| Term | Meaning | Signs Include |
|---|---|---|
| Over trading | *Too little working capital* | *Rapidly increasing sales volumes*<br>*Payment made to late to suppl.* |
| Over capitalization | *Too much working capital* | *High cash balance*<br>*Payment made to supplier before they are due* |

Options for '**Meaning**':

■ Too much working capital

■ Too little working capital

■ The right amount of working capital

Options for '**Signs Include**':

■ Rapidly increasing sales volumes ✓

■ Reduced value of receivables (debtors)

■ High cash balances ✓

■ Payments made to suppliers before they are due ✓

■ Overdrawn bank balances

■ Payments made late to suppliers ✓

■ Increased profit margins

**1.3** Select from the following statements, those that are correct.

|  |  | True | False |
|---|---|:---:|:---:|
| (a) | Receipts that relate to the proceeds from the disposal of non-current (fixed) assets are capital receipts. | ✓ | |
| (b) | Payments that relate to the acquisition of non-current (fixed) assets are regular revenue payments. | | ✓ |
| (c) | Payments made to the owners of the business are capital receipts. | | ✓ |
| (d) | Income received from the operating activities of the business that is expected to occur frequently is a regular revenue receipt. | ✓ | |
| (e) | Income received from the operating activities of the business that is not expected to occur frequently is a regular revenue receipt. | | ✓ |
| (f) | Payments arising from the operating activities of the business that are expected to occur frequently are regular revenue payments. | ✓ | |
| (g) | Payments that relate to the acquisition of non-current (fixed) assets are capital payments.. | | ✓ |
| (h) | The receipt of a bank loan is an example of an exceptional receipt. | ✓ | |

**1.4** A business currently has the following features:

- Sales are increasing, leading to increased receivables (debtors)
- Inventory (stock) is being increased to satisfy increased demand
- Payments to suppliers are being delayed due to a shortage of cash

Is the business likely to be experiencing

| | | ✓ |
|---|---|:---:|
| (a) | Over capitalization | |
| (b) | Normal trading | |
| (c) | Over trading | ✓ |
| (d) | Stagnation | |

**1.5** Complete the following table by ticking the appropriate column to indicate the category of each payment example.

✓

| Example | Capital payment | Regular revenue payment | Payment for drawings | Exceptional payment |
|---|---|---|---|---|
| Dividends | | | | |
| Acquisition of new business | | | | |
| Purchase of raw materials | | | | |
| Purchase of computer | | | | |
| Payment of Corporation Tax | | | | |
| Repayment of whole loan | | | | |

# 2 Chapter activities
## Preparing cash budgets

**2.1** Martha owns a greengrocer's shop and prepares annual income statements and statements of financial position. These are prepared on an accruals basis.

Since the fruit and vegetables that she sells are perishable, no inventory (stock) is held at the year end (when the business is closed over the holiday period). Some sales are made on a cash basis and some on a credit basis. All purchases are made on credit terms.

The income statement for Martha's business for the year ended 31 December 20-5 is as follows:

|  | £ | £ |
| --- | --- | --- |
| Sales |  | 128,900 |
| Less: Purchases |  | (50,060) |
| Gross profit |  | 78,840 |
| Less: Expenses |  |  |
| Wages | 21,400 |  |
| Rent of shop | 12,000 |  |
| Shop expenses | 5,350 |  |
| Depreciation of shop fittings | 500 |  |
| Bank charges | 350 |  |
|  |  | 39,600 |
|  |  | 39,240 |

During 20-5, Martha took £20,000 from the business in drawings

Extracts from the statements of financial position at 31 December 20-4 and 31 December 20-5 show the following:

| Statement of financial position at | 31 Dec 20-4 | 31 Dec 20-5 |
| --- | --- | --- |
|  | £ | £ |
| Trade Receivables (debtors) | 1,200 | 1,840 |
| Trade Payables (creditors) | 8,900 | 7,630 |
| Accruals – shop expenses | 190 | 210 |
| Accruals – bank charges | 0 | 50 |
| Prepayments – rent of shop | 1,200 | 1,500 |

Calculate the actual business cash receipts and cash payments for the year to 31 December 20-5.

| | £ |
|---|---|
| Sales receipts | 128 260 |
| Purchases payments | ( 51 330 ) |
| Wages paid | 21 400 |
| Rent paid | 12 300 |
| Shop expenses | 5 330 |
| Depreciation | nil |
| Bank charges | 300 |
| Drawings | 20 000 |

**2.2** The cash budget for Haven Industries for the three months ended June has been partially completed. The following information is to be incorporated and the cash budget completed.

■ A bank loan of £52,800 has been negotiated and this will be paid into the business bank account in April.

■ The principal (capital) element of the bank loan (£52,800) is to be repaid in 48 equal monthly installments beginning in May.

■ The loan attracts 12% interest per annum calculated on the amount of the loan principal advanced in April. The annual interest charge is to be paid in equal monthly installments beginning in May.

■ When Haven Industries uses its bank overdraft facility interest is payable monthly and is estimated at 2% of the previous months overdraft balance. The interest is to be rounded to the nearest £.

■ At 1 April the balance of the bank account was £1,750

Using the additional information above, complete the cash budget for Haven Industries for the three months ending June. Cash inflows should be entered as positive figures and cash outflows as negative figures. Zeroes must be entered where appropriate to achieve full marks.

| | April £ | May £ | June £ |
|---|---|---|---|
| **RECEIPTS** | | | |
| Cash sales | 8,800 | 9,180 | 10,480 |
| Credit sales | 53,085 | 53,520 | 64,852 |
| Bank loan | 52800 | 0 | 0 |
| **Total receipts** | 114685 | 67700 | 75332 |
| | | | |
| **PAYMENTS** | | | |
| Purchases | -36,650 | -37,005 | -42,075 |
| Wages | -18,800 | -18,950 | -18,450 |
| Expenses | -10,350 | -11,260 | -13,260 |
| Capital expenditure | 0 | -59,500 | 0 |
| Bank loan capital repayment | 0 | 1100 | 1100 |
| Bank loan interest | 0 | 447 | 447 |
| Overdraft interest | 0 | 35 | 193 |
| **Total payments** | 65800 | 127997 | 74235 |
| Net cash flow | 48885 | -60297 | 1097 |
| Opening bank balance | 1750 | 50635 | -9662 |
| **Closing bank balance** | 50635 | -9662 | -8565 |

**2.3** Minor Enterprises Limited has been trading for a number of years. The business has requested assistance with calculating sales receipts for entry into a cash budget.

Actual sales values achieved are available for January and February and forecast sales values have been produced for March to June.

Minor Enterprises Limited estimates that cash sales account for 30% of the total sales. The remaining 70% of sales are made on a credit basis.

**(a)** Complete the table below to show the split of total sales between cash sales and credit sales.

|  | Actual | | Forecast | | | |
|---|---|---|---|---|---|---|
|  | January | February | March | April | May | June |
| Total sales | 18,500 | 19,600 | 19,100 | 22,000 | 21,600 | 23,400 |
|  |  |  |  |  |  |  |
| Cash sales | 5550 | 5880 | 5730 | 6600 | 6480 | 7020 |
|  |  |  |  |  |  |  |
| Credit sales | 12950 | 13720 | 13370 | 15400 | 15120 | 16380 |

**(b)** Minor Enterprises estimates that 60% of credit sales are received in the month after sale with the balance being received two months after sale. For example, 60% of January's credit sales are received in February with the balance being received in March.

Using the table below and your figures from part (a), calculate the timing of sales receipts from credit sales that would be included in a cash budget for Minor Enterprises Limited for the period March to June.

|  | Credit sales £ |  | Cash received | | | | |
|---|---|---|---|---|---|---|---|
|  |  |  | February £ | March £ | April £ | May £ | June £ |
| January | 12950 |  | 7770 | 5180 |  |  |  |
| February | 13720 |  |  | 8232 | 5488 |  |  |
| March | 13370 |  |  |  | 8022 | 5348 |  |
| April | 15400 |  |  |  |  | 9240 | 6160 |
| May | 15120 |  |  |  |  |  | 9072 |
| Monthly credit sales receipts |  |  |  | 13412 | 13510 | 14588 | 15232 |

**2.4** Bishopswood Ltd is preparing cash payment figures ready for inclusion in a cash budget. The following information is relevant to the payment patterns for purchases, wages and expenses.

■ Purchases are calculated as 65% of the next month's forecast sales and are paid two months after the date of purchase. For example, purchases in July are based on the estimated sales for August and paid for in September.

|  | Actual | | | Forecast | | |
|---|---|---|---|---|---|---|
|  | **July** | **August** | **September** | **October** | **November** | **December** |
|  | £ | £ | £ | £ | £ | £ |
| Total sales | 71,000 | 77,800 | 76,200 | 80,000 | 85,000 | 87,000 |

■ Wages are paid in the month that they are incurred and expenses are paid in the month after they are incurred. The actual and forecast figures for wages and expenses are:

|  | Actual | | | Forecast | | |
|---|---|---|---|---|---|---|
|  | **July** | **August** | **September** | **October** | **November** | **December** |
|  | £ | £ | £ | £ | £ | £ |
| Wages | 8,500 | 8,750 | 9,000 | 8,800 | 8,700 | 8,950 |
| Expenses (excluding depreciation) | 7,450 | 9,010 | 6,450 | 7,100 | 8,050 | 7,300 |

■ A new machine is to be purchased in October at a total cost of £40,500. Payment for the machine is to be made in three equal monthly installments, beginning in October.

■ The machine is to be depreciated monthly on a straight-line basis at 20% per annum.

Prepare an extract of the payments section of the cash budget for Bishopswood Ltd for the three months ended December.

|  | October | November | December |
|---|---|---|---|
|  | £ | £ | £ |
| **PAYMENTS** |  |  |  |
| Purchases | 49 530 | 52 000 | 55 250 |
| Wages | 8 800 | 8 700 | 8 950 |
| Expenses | 6 450 | 7 100 | 8 050 |
| New machine | 13 500 | 13 500 | 13 500 |
| **Total payments** | 78 280 | 81 300 | 85 750 |

# Chapter activities
**3**
# Forecasting data for cash budgets

**3.1** Freddo Limited is preparing its forecast sales and purchase information for January of next year.

The sales volume trend is to be identified using a 3-point moving average based on the actual monthly sales volumes for the current year.

**(a)** Complete the table below to calculate the monthly sales volume trend and identify any monthly variations.

| | Sales volume (units) | Trend | Monthly variation (volume less trend) |
|---|---|---|---|
| August | 56,160 | | |
| | | | |
| September | 35,640 | 41040 | −5400 |
| | | | |
| October | 31,320 | 42120 | − 10 800 |
| | | | |
| November | 59,400 | 43200 | 16 200 |
| | | | |
| December | 38,880 | | − 54 |

The monthly sales volume trend is | 1080 | units.

### Additional information

- The selling price per unit has been set at £5.
- Monthly purchases are estimated to be 60% of the value of the forecast sales.
- The seasonal variations operate on a 3 month repeating cycle.

**(b)** Using the trend and the monthly variations identified in part a. complete the table below to forecast the sales volume, sales value and purchase value for January of the next financial year.

| | Forecast trend | Variation | Forecast sales volume | Forecast sales £ | Forecast purchases £ |
|---|---|---|---|---|---|
| January | 45360 | − 10800 | 34560 | 172800 | 103680 |

**3.2** Freddo Limited uses an industry wage rate index to forecast future monthly wage costs. Employees receive a pay increase in April each year, based on the index for the previous month (March). The current monthly wage cost of £18,620 was calculated based on a wage index of 326. The forecast wage rate index for the next four months is:

| | |
|---|---|
| January | 361 |
| February | 370 |
| March | 379 |
| April | 385 |

If the company uses the forecast wage rate index, what will the wage cost for April be, to the nearest £? (Select one)

| | |
|---|---|
| (a) £21,990 | ✓ |
| (b) £16,016 | |
| (c) £19,548 | |
| (d) £21,647 | |

**3.3** Deanswood Limited operates a five day week. The data shown in the following table relates to sales in units over a two week period.

**(a)** Complete the table to show the trend (calculated on a five point moving average) and the daily variations (volume less trend).

| Day | Sales units | Trend | Variations |
|---|---|---|---|
| Monday | 170 | | |
| Tuesday | 185 | | |
| Wednesday | 200 | 210 | −10 |
| Thursday | 240 | ~~1045~~ 215 | 25 |
| Friday | 255 | 220 | 35 |
| Monday | 195 | 225 | −30 |
| Tuesday | 210 | 230 | −20 |
| Wednesday | 225 | 235 | −10 |
| Thursday | 265 | 240 | 25 |
| Friday | 280 | 2~~45~~ 250 255 | 35 −30 −20 |

**(b)** Variations operate on a repeating cycle. Forecast the trend, variation and sales in units for Monday of the following week, using the table below.

| Day | Forecast Trend | Forecast Variation | Forecast Sales |
|---|---|---|---|
| Monday | 260 | − 10 | 250 |

**3.4**   The cost of an electronic component has been falling by an average of 2% every six months. In January 20-5 the cost of the component is £50. Assuming the cost continues to behave in the same way in future, what is the forecast cost in July 20-6?

| | ✓ |
|---|---|
| (a)  £47.00 | |
| (b)  £48.00 | |
| (c)  £48.02 | ✓ |
| (d)  £47.06 | |

*Jan. 50  Jul - Dec 49*

*Jan Jun  48.02*

**3.5**   Chocco Limited is forecasting the cost of a certain type of cocoa, which is one of the raw materials for its chocolate products. The cost was £1,890 per tonne in April 20-1. The following index data (actual and forecast) is available:

| | Consumer Price Index | Raw Cocoa Price Index |
|---|---|---|
| April 20-1 Actual | 471 | 163 |
| April 20-2 Forecast | 485 | 194 |

Using the most appropriate data, forecast the cost per tonne of cocoa in April 20-2 to the nearest £.

| |
|---|
| £ |

**4.2** The quarterly budgeted and actual figures for an organisation are provided below:

|  | Budgeted | Actual |
|---|---|---|
|  | £ | £ |
| Receipts from credit customers | 95,340 | 93,260 |
| Cash sales | 20,150 | 15,400 |
| Payments to credit suppliers | (54,900) | (63,150) |
| Cash purchases | (4,500) | (3,450) |
| Capital expenditure | (18,500) | - |
| Wages and salaries | (18,600) | (18,300) |
| General expenses | (28,500) | (31,464) |
| Net cash flow | (9,510) | (7,704) |
| Opening bank balance | 14,200 | 14,200 |
| Closing bank balance | 4,690 | 6,496 |

Prepare a reconciliation of budgeted cash flow with actual cash flow for the quarter. Select the appropriate description for each entry, and show + or − signs to denote increased or reduced cash. Ensure that the reconciliation balances.

|  | £ |
|---|---|
| Budgeted closing bank balance | 4690 |
| Surplus/Shortfall in receipts from credit customers | 2080 |
| Surplus/Shortfall in cash sales | 4750 |
| Increase/Decrease in payments to credit suppliers | − 8250 |
| Increase/Decrease in cash purchases | −1050 |
| Increase/Decrease in capital expenditure | −18500 |
| Increase/Decrease in wages and salaries | −300 |
| Increase/Decrease in general expenses | −2964 |
| Actual closing bank balance | 6496 |

**4.3**   Variances between budget and actual cash flows can occur for a number of reasons. There are also a variety of courses of action available to minimise adverse variances or benefit from favourable variances.

Match each cause of a variance listed on the left with a possible course of action on the right.

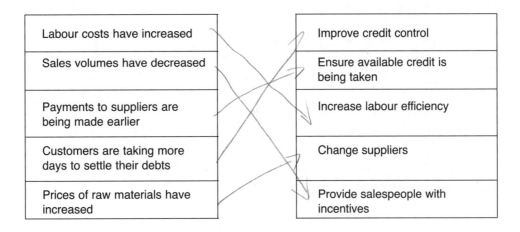

| | |
|---|---|
| Labour costs have increased | Improve credit control |
| Sales volumes have decreased | Ensure available credit is being taken |
| Payments to suppliers are being made earlier | Increase labour efficiency |
| Customers are taking more days to settle their debts | Change suppliers |
| Prices of raw materials have increased | Provide salespeople with incentives |

**4.4**   A company buys and sells products, with a gross profit margin of 40%. The company is considering changes in its policy, so that

■    customers will be required to pay in two months instead of the current three months, and

■    suppliers will be paid in one month instead of the current two months.

Assuming that this policy is operated, and there is no change to the prices or volumes, which of the following statements is correct?

✓

| | |
|---|---|
| (a) The cash position of the company will deteriorate | |
| (b) The cash position of the company will improve | |
| (c) The cash position of the company will not be affected | ✓ |
| (d) It is impossible to determine the effect of these changes on the cash position of the company | |

## 5   Chapter activities
## Managing liquidity – the UK financial system

**5.1**   A symptom of lack of liquidity in a business is:

| | ✔ |
|---|---|
| the inability of the business to pay its suppliers | ✓ |
| the inability of its customers to settle their accounts | ✓ |
| a major reduction in the overdraft of the company | |

Select the correct option

**5.2**   The functions of the Bank of England include the following:

| | ✔ |
|---|---|
| it is the Central Bank of the UK | ✓ |
| it is in charge of the financial services industry | |
| it helps to influence interest rates in the economy | ✓ |

Select the correct **two** options

**5.3**   The interbank market is a money market where

| | ✔ |
|---|---|
| bank customers pay large sums of money to each other using the banking system | ✓ |
| banks make large short-term loans to each other | |
| money brokers trade bank shares with each other on behalf of clients | |

Select the correct option

**5.4** Banks must maintain liquidity so that they can

| | ✔ |
|---|---|
| provide funds for the Bank of England | |
| maintain an acceptable level of profitability | |
| repay customer deposits if they are required to do so | ✓ |

Select the correct option

**5.5** The Bank of England helps to control inflation in the economy through the Monetary Control Committee by

| | ✔ |
|---|---|
| setting short-term interest rates | ✓ |
| setting long-term interest rates | |
| adjusting the UK Gold Reserves | |

Select the correct option

**5.6** A rise in interest rates in the UK economy will normally

| | ✔ |
|---|---|
| increase business activity because more businesses will be able to borrow | |
| decrease business activity because businesses will be less likely to borrow | ✓ |
| have no effect at all on business activity | |

Select the correct option

# 6   Chapter activities
## Managing liquidity – raising finance from the bank

**6.1**   The main advantage to a customer of a bank overdraft is:

| | ✔ |
|---|---|
| the customer only borrows what is needed | |
| the limit will vary on a daily basis | |
| no security is needed by the bank | ✓ |

Select the correct option

**6.2**   A 'variable' interest rate on a bank business loan means that the rate:

| | ✔ |
|---|---|
| varies according to the amount left outstanding on the loan | |
| varies according to the length of time left until final repayment | |
| is based on the bank lending rate, which varies over time | ✓ |

Select the correct option

**6.3**   The legal position of a bank that takes a mortgage over a customer's property is that of

| | ✔ |
|---|---|
| mortgagor | ✓ |
| mortgagee | |
| guarantor | |

Select the correct option

**6.4**   A fixed and floating charge taken as security is only suitable for a business that is set up as a

| | ✔ |
|---|---|
| sole trader | |
| partnership | |
| limited company | ✔ |

Select the correct option

**6.5**   A business borrowing by means of a bank overdraft can calculate the interest payable for cash flow forecast purposes by

| | ✔ |
|---|---|
| applying the interest rate chargeable by the bank to the projected average overdrawn balance for the period | |
| applying the interest rate chargeable by the bank to the projected average daily balance for the period | |
| using the figure for interest paid on the overdraft for the comparable period in the previous financial year | |

Select the correct option

**6.6**   A business borrowing by means of a fixed rate bank loan which is repaid in full at the end of the loan period, will pay, on the basis of the same interest rate

| | ✔ |
|---|---|
| less interest on the loan than an ordinary monthly instalment repayment loan | |
| a larger amount of interest on the loan than an ordinary monthly instalment repayment loan | |
| exactly the same amount of interest as  an ordinary monthly instalment repayment loan | ✔ |

Select the correct option

# 7

## Chapter activities

## Managing liquidity – investing surplus funds

**7.1** A company Treasury Department has the option of investing £500,000 on the money markets. The highest interest rate is likely to be received from an investment that is

| | ✔ |
|---|---|
| low risk and for a longer period | |
| higher risk and for a longer period | ✔ |
| low risk and for a shorter period | |

Select the correct option

**7.2** For the three options given below, the lowest rate of interest given on the London money markets is likely to be given by

| | ✔ |
|---|---|
| a Treasury Bill | ✔ |
| a Certificate of Deposit | |
| an interbank deposit | |

Select the correct option

**7.3** Gilt-edged stock (Gilts) are certificates

| | ✔ |
|---|---|
| issued by the banks and given a guaranteed repayment amount | |
| issued by the Government and given a return based on the sterling exchange rate | |
| issued by the Government and therefore very low risk | ✔ |

**7.4**   A business is interested in investing in some Government stock. The details are as follows:

interest rate                                    7%

redemption date                            2016

price                         £1.31 per £1 of stock

The current interest yield is:

| | ✔ |
|---|---|
| 5.34% | |
| 1.40% | ✔ |
| 1.22% | |

Select the correct option

**7.5**   The running of a company Treasury should be regulated by a set of Policies and Procedures which will ensure that the company's surplus funds are invested in a way which minimises risk.

Indicate with a tick which of the following regulations is likely to be found in the company regulations:

| | ✔ |
|---|---|
| investment limits for various levels of employees and managers | |
| the permissible types of investment | |
| a minimum requirement for very liquid funds, eg 7 days or less | |
| Bank of England permission to invest in Treasury Bills and Gilts | ✔ |

Select all the correct options

# Answers to chapter activities

# 1 Chapter activities – answers
# Managing cash flows

**1.1** **(a)**

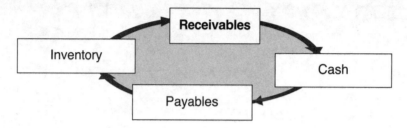

**(b)** The cash operating cycle is 70 days.

**1.2**

| Term | Meaning | Signs Include |
|---|---|---|
| Over trading | Too little working capital | Rapidly increasing sales volumes<br>Overdrawn bank balances<br>Payments made late to suppliers |
| Over capitalization | Too much working capital | High cash balances<br>Payments made to suppliers before they are due |

**1.3**

| | | True | False |
|---|---|---|---|
| (a) | Receipts that relate to the proceeds from the disposal of non-current assets are capital receipts. | ✓ | |
| (b) | Payments that relate to the acquisition of non-current assets are regular revenue payments. | | ✓ |
| (c) | Payments made to the owners of the business are capital receipts. | | ✓ |
| (d) | Income received from the operating activities of the business that is expected to occur frequently is a regular revenue receipt. | ✓ | |
| (e) | Income received from the operating activities of the business that is not expected to occur frequently is a regular revenue receipt. | | ✓ |
| (f) | Payments arising from the operating activities of the business that are expected to occur frequently are regular revenue payments | ✓ | |
| (g) | Payments that relate to the acquisition of non-current assets are capital payments. | ✓ | |
| (h) | The receipt of a bank loan is an example of an exceptional receipt. | ✓ | |

**1.4**   The business likely to be experiencing  (c)  Over trading

**1.5**

| Example | Capital payment | Regular revenue payment | Payment for drawings | Exceptional payment |
|---|---|---|---|---|
| Dividends | | | ✓ | |
| Acquisition of new business | | | | ✓ |
| Purchase of raw materials | | ✓ | | |
| Purchase of computer | ✓ | | | |
| Payment of Corporation Tax | | ✓ | | |
| Repayment of whole loan | | | | ✓ |

# 2  Chapter activities – answers
# Preparing cash budgets

**2.1**

| | £ | Workings (£) |
|---|---|---|
| Sales receipts | 128,260 | 128,900 + 1,200 − 1,840 |
| Purchases payments | 51,330 | 50,060 + 8,900 − 7,630 |
| Wages paid | 21,400 | No adjustments |
| Rent paid | 12,300 | 12,000 − 1,200 + 1,500 |
| Shop expenses | 5,330 | 5,350 + 190 - 210 |
| Depreciation | 0 | Non cash item |
| Bank charges | 300 | 350 - 50 |
| Drawings | 20,000 | Per narrative |

**2.2**

|  | April £ | May £ | June £ |
|---|---|---|---|
| **RECEIPTS** | | | |
| Cash sales | 8,800 | 9,180 | 10,480 |
| Credit sales | 53,085 | 53,520 | 64,852 |
| Bank loan | 52,800 | 0 | 0 |
| **Total receipts** | **114,685** | **62,700** | **75,332** |
| **PAYMENTS** | | | |
| Purchases | -36,650 | -37,005 | -42,075 |
| Wages | -18,800 | -18,950 | -18,450 |
| Expenses | -10,350 | -11,260 | -13,260 |
| Capital expenditure | 0 | -59,500 | 0 |
| Bank loan capital repayment | 0 | -1,100 | -1,100 |
| Bank loan interest | 0 | -528 | -528 |
| Overdraft interest | 0 | 0 | -300 |
| Total payments | -65,800 | -128,343 | -75,713 |
| Net cash flow | 48,885 | -65,643 | -381 |
| Opening bank balance | 1,750 | 50,635 | -15,008 |
| **Closing bank balance** | 50,635 | -15,008 | -15,389 |

**2.3** **(a)**

|  | Actual | | Forecast | | | |
|---|---|---|---|---|---|---|
|  | January | February | March | April | May | June |
| Total sales | 18,500 | 19,600 | 19,100 | 22,000 | 21,600 | 23,400 |
| | | | | | | |
| Cash sales | 5,550 | 5,880 | 5,730 | 6,600 | 6,480 | 7,020 |
| | | | | | | |
| Credit sales | 12,950 | 13,720 | 13,370 | 15,400 | 15,120 | 16,380 |

**(b)**

| | Credit sales | Cash received February | March | April | May | June |
|---|---|---|---|---|---|---|
| | £ | £ | £ | £ | £ | £ |
| January | 12,950 | 7,770 | 5,180 | | | |
| February | 13,720 | | 8,232 | 5,488 | | |
| March | 13,370 | | | 8,022 | 5,348 | |
| April | 15,400 | | | | 9,240 | 6,160 |
| May | 15,120 | | | | | 9,072 |
| Monthly credit sales receipts | | | 13,412 | 13,510 | 14,588 | 15,232 |

**2.4**

| | October | November | December |
|---|---|---|---|
| | £ | £ | £ |
| **PAYMENTS** | | | |
| Purchases | 49,530 | 52,000 | 55,250 |
| Wages | 8,800 | 8,700 | 8,950 |
| Expenses | 6,450 | 7,100 | 8,050 |
| New machine | 13,500 | 13,500 | 13,500 |
| **Total payments** | 78,280 | 81,300 | 85,750 |

# 3

## Chapter activities – answers
## Forecasting data for cash budgets

**3.1** **(a)**

|  | Sales volume (units) | Trend | Monthly variation (volume less trend) |
|---|---|---|---|
| August | 56,160 |  |  |
|  |  |  |  |
| September | 35,640 | 41,040 | -5,400 |
|  |  |  |  |
| October | 31,320 | 42,120 | -10,800 |
|  |  |  |  |
| November | 59,400 | 43,200 | 16,200 |
|  |  |  |  |
| December | 38,880 |  |  |

The monthly sales volume trend is 1,080 units.

**(b)**

|  | Forecast trend | Variation | Forecast sales volume | Forecast sales £ | Forecast purchases £ |
|---|---|---|---|---|---|
| January | 45,360 | -10,800 | 34,560 | 172,800 | 103,680 |

**3.2** **(d)** £21,647

**3.3** **(a)**

| | Sales units | Trend | Variations |
|---|---|---|---|
| Monday | 170 | | |
| Tuesday | 185 | | |
| Wednesday | 200 | 210 | -10 |
| Thursday | 240 | 215 | +25 |
| Friday | 255 | 220 | +35 |
| Monday | 195 | 225 | -30 |
| Tuesday | 210 | 230 | -20 |
| Wednesday | 225 | 235 | -10 |
| Thursday | 265 | *240* | |
| Friday | 280 | *245* | |

*250        255*

**(b)**

| Day | Forecast Trend | Forecast Variation | Forecast Sales |
|---|---|---|---|
| Monday | 250 | -30 | 220 |

**3.4** (d)  £47.06

**3.5**  £2,249

# 4 Chapter activities – answers
# Using cash budgets

## 4.1 (a)

|  | Period 1 (£) | Period 2 (£) | Period 3 (£) | Period 4 (£) | Period 5 (£) |
|---|---|---|---|---|---|
| Original value of forecast sales | 63,000 | 61,500 | 66,000 | 67,500 | 69,000 |
|  |  |  |  |  |  |
| Original timing of receipts |  |  | 63,750 | 66,750 | 68,250 |
| Revised value of forecast sales | 56,700 | 55,350 | 59,400 | 60,750 | 62,100 |
|  |  |  |  |  |  |
| Revised timing of receipts |  |  | 56,835 | 58,995 | 60,885 |

### (b)

|  | Period 3 (£) | Period 4 (£) | Period 5 (£) |
|---|---|---|---|
| Original timing of payments | 31,200 | 30,800 | 32,000 |
| Revised timing of payments | 37,360 | 31,040 | 32,200 |

### (c)

|  | Period 3 (£) | Period 4 (£) | Period 5 (£) |
|---|---|---|---|
| Changes in sales receipts | -6,915 | -7,755 | -7,365 |
| Changes in purchase payments | -6,160 | -240 | -200 |
| Net change | -13,075 | -7,995 | -7,565 |

**4.2**

|  | £ |
|---|---|
| Budgeted closing bank balance | 4,690 |
| Shortfall in receipts from credit customers | -2,080 |
| Shortfall in cash sales | -4,750 |
| Increase in payments to credit suppliers | -8,250 |
| Decrease in cash purchases | +1,050 |
| Decrease in capital expenditure | +18,500 |
| Decrease in wages and salaries | +300 |
| Increase in general expenses | -2,964 |
| Actual closing bank balance | 6,496 |

**4.3**

Labour costs have increased ➡ Increase labour efficiency

Sales volumes have decreased ➡ Provide salespeople with incentives

Payments to suppliers are being made earlier ➡ Ensure available credit is being taken

Customers are taking more days to settle their debts ➡ Improve credit control

Prices of raw materials have increased ➡ Change suppliers

**4.4** Assuming that this policy is operated, and there is no change to the prices or volumes, the following statements is correct:

(b) The cash position of the company will improve

(The increase in cash due to the reduced receivables will be greater that the decrease in cash due to the reduced payables)

# 5 Chapter activities – answers
# Managing liquidity – the UK financial system

**5.1**   the inability of the business to pay its suppliers

**5.2**   it is the Central Bank of the UK

   it helps to influence interest rates in the economy

**5.3**   banks make large short-term loans to each other

**5.4**   repay customer deposits if they are required to do so

**5.5**   setting short-term interest rates

**5.6**   decrease business activity because businesses will be less likely to borrow

# 6 Chapter activities
# Managing liquidity – raising finance from the bank

**6.1**    the customer only borrows what is needed

**6.2**    is based on the bank lending rate, which varies over time

**6.3**    mortgagee

**6.4**    limited company

**6.5**    applying the interest rate chargeable by the bank to the projected average overdrawn balance for the period

**6.6**    a larger amount of interest on the loan than an ordinary monthly instalment repayment loan

# 7 Chapter activities – answers
# Managing liquidity – investing surplus funds

**7.1**   higher risk and for a longer period

**7.2**   a Treasury Bill

**7.3**   issued by the Government and therefore very low risk

**7.4**   5.34%

**7.5**   investment limits for various levels of employees and managers

the permissible types of investment

a minimum requirement for very liquid funds, eg 7 days or less

# Cash management

# Practice assessment 1

## SECTION 1

**Task 1.1**

**(a)** Complete the diagram below of the working capital cycle by placing the options into the correct boxes.

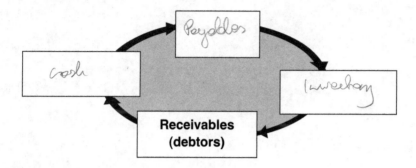

**Options:**

■ Payables (creditors)

■ Cash

■ Inventory (stock)

**(b)** A business has an average inventory (stock) holding period of 70 days. It receives payment from its customers in 96 days and pays its suppliers in 45 days.

What is the cash operating cycle in days for the business? (Select one).

| | ✓ |
|---|---|
| 71 days | |
| 121 days | ✓ |
| 19 days | |
| 211 days | |

**(c)** Complete the following sentences by selecting the correct options:

Over-capitalisation can occur when a business has **[too much/insufficient]** working capital and over-trading can occur when a business has **[too much/insufficient]** working capital.

Signs of over-capitalisation include **[high/low/normal]** inventory (stock) levels, **[high/low/normal]** cash levels, **[high/low/normal]** receivables (debtors) levels, and suppliers being paid **[early/late/on time]**.

**Task 1.2**

(a)    Complete the following table by ticking the appropriate column to indicate the category of each payment example.

✓

| Example | Capital payment | Regular revenue payment | Payment for drawings | Exceptional payment |
|---|---|---|---|---|
| Purchase of machinery | ✓ | | | ✓ |
| Loan repayments | | | | ✓ |
| Purchase of shares to take over another company | | | ✓ | |
| Final dividends | | | | ✓ |
| Salary payments | | ✓ | | |
| Bank interest payments | | ✓ | | |

(b)    Posy is a florist, and prepares annual income statements (profit and loss accounts) and statements of financial position (balance sheets). These are prepared on an accruals basis.

Since the flowers that she sells are perishable, no inventory (stock) is held at the year end (when the business is closed over the holiday period). Most sales are made on a cash basis, but some are on a credit basis. All purchases are made on credit terms.

The income statement for Posy's business for the year ended 31 December 20-5 is as follows:

|  | £ | £ |
|---|---|---|
| Sales | | 103,900 |
| Less: Purchases | | (45,090) |
| Gross profit | | 58,810 |
| Less: Expenses | | |
| Wages | 26,430 | |
| Rent of shop | 9,000 | |
| Shop expenses | 5,950 | |
| Depreciation of shop fittings | 600 | |
| Bank interest | 190 | |
| | | 42,170 |
| | | 16,640 |

During 20-5, Posy took £15,000 from the business in drawings.

Extracts from the statements of financial position at 31 December 20-4 and 31 December 20-5 show the following:

| Statement of financial position at | 31 Dec 20-4 | 31 Dec 20-5 |
|---|---|---|
| | £ | £ |
| Trade Receivables (debtors) | 680 | 840 |
| Trade Payables (creditors) | 8,450 | 7,930 |
| Accruals – shop expenses | 120 | 210 |
| Accruals – bank interest | 55 | 0 |
| Prepayments – rent of shop | 1,500 | 1,000 |

Calculate the actual business cash receipts and cash payments for the year to 31 December 20-5.

| | £ |
|---|---|
| Sales receipts | 103740 |
| Purchases payments | 45610 |
| Wages paid | 26430 |
| Rent paid | 8500 |
| Shop expenses | 5860 |
| Depreciation | nil |
| Bank interest | 245 |
| Drawings | 15000 |

**Task 1.3**

Chapter Limited is preparing its forecast sales and purchase information for January of next year.

The sales volume trend is to be identified using a 3-point moving average based on the actual monthly sales volumes for the current year.

(a)    Complete the table below to calculate the monthly sales volume trend and identify any monthly variations.

| | Sales volume (units) | Trend | Monthly variation (volume less trend) |
|---|---|---|---|
| August | 40,900 | | |
| | | | |
| September | 47,300 | 42300 | 5000 |
| | | | |
| October | 38,700 | 42600 | - 3900 |
| | | | |
| November | 41,800 | 42900 | - 1100 |
| | | | |
| December | 48,200 | 43200 | 5000 |

The monthly sales volume trend is [ 300 ] units.

**Additional information**

The selling price per unit has been set at £8.

Monthly purchases are estimated to be 55% of the value of the forecast sales.

The seasonal variations operate on a 3 month repeating cycle

(b)    Using the trend and the monthly variations identified in part (a) complete the table below to forecast the sales volume, sales value and purchase value for January of the next financial year.

| | Forecast trend | Variation | Forecast sales volume | Forecast sales £ | Forecast purchases £ |
|---|---|---|---|---|---|
| January | 43500 | - 3900 | 39600 | 316800 | 174240 |

**(c)** Chapter Limited uses an industry wage rate index to forecast future monthly wage costs. Employees receive a pay increase in January each year, based on the index for that month. The current monthly wage cost of £23,650 was calculated based on a wage index of 637. The forecast wage rate index for the next four months is:

| | |
|---|---|
| November | 642 |
| December | 643 |
| January | 648 |
| February | 647 |

If the company uses the forecast wage rate index, what will the wage cost for January be, to the nearest £? (Select one)

| | |
|---|---|
| £24,058 | ✓ |
| £23,249 | |
| £23,834 | |
| £23,873 | |

**Task 1.4**

Captain Enterprises Limited has been trading for a number of years. The business has requested assistance with calculating sales receipts for entry into a cash budget.

Actual sales values achieved are available for January and February and forecast sales values have been produced for March to June.

Captain Enterprises Limited estimates that cash sales account for 25% of the total sales. The remaining 75% of sales are made on a credit basis.

**(a)** Complete the table below to show the split of total sales between cash sales and credit sales.

| | Actual | | Forecast | | | |
|---|---|---|---|---|---|---|
| | **January** | **February** | **March** | **April** | **May** | **June** |
| Total sales | 48,100 | 49,600 | 49,000 | 52,500 | 51,600 | 49,400 |
| | | | | | | |
| Cash sales | 12025 | 12400 | 12250 | 13125 | 12900 | 12350 |
| | | | | | | |
| Credit sales | 36075 | 37200 | 36750 | 39375 | 38700 | 37050 |

**(b)** Captain Enterprises estimates that 40% of credit sales are received in the month after sale with the balance being received two months after sale. For example, 40% of January's credit sales are received in February with the balance being received in March.

Using the table below and your figures from part (a), calculate the timing of sales receipts from credit sales that would be included in a cash budget for Captain Enterprises Limited for the period March to June.

| | Credit sales £ | | CASH RECEIVED February £ | March £ | April £ | May £ | June £ |
|---|---|---|---|---|---|---|---|
| January | 36075 | | 14430 | 21645 | | | |
| February | 37200 | | | 14880 | 22320 | | |
| March | 36750 | | | | 14700 | 22050 | |
| April | 39375 | | | | | 15750 | 23625 |
| May | 38700 | | | | | | 15480 |
| Monthly credit sales receipts | | | | 36525 | 37020 | 37800 | 39105 |

**Task 1.5**

Queenswood Ltd is preparing cash payment figures ready for inclusion in a cash budget. The following information is relevant to the payment patterns for purchases, wages and expenses.

■ Purchases are calculated as 58% of the next month's forecast sales and are paid two months after the date of purchase. For example, purchases in July are based on the estimated sales for August and paid for in September.

| | Actual | | | Forecast | | |
|---|---|---|---|---|---|---|
| | July | August | September | October | November | December |
| | £ | £ | £ | £ | £ | £ |
| Total sales | 79,000 | 83,800 | 86,200 | 90,600 | 95,000 | 97,200 |

■ Wages are paid in the month that they are incurred and expenses are paid in the month after they are incurred. The actual and forecast figures for wages and expenses are:

| | Actual | | | Forecast | | |
|---|---|---|---|---|---|---|
| | July | August | September | October | November | December |
| | £ | £ | £ | £ | £ | £ |
| Wages | 12,500 | 12,600 | 12,480 | 12,800 | 12,960 | 14,500 |
| Expenses (excluding depreciation) | 8,640 | 8,800 | 9,050 | 7,450 | 10,100 | 9,300 |

■ A new machine is to be purchased in October at a total cost of £53,500. Payment for the machine is to be made in four equal monthly installments, beginning in October.

■ The machine is to be depreciated monthly on a straight-line basis at 25% per annum.

Prepare an extract of the payments section of the cash budget for Queenswood Ltd for the three months ended December.

| | October £ | November £ | December £ |
|---|---|---|---|
| **PAYMENTS** | u | | |
| Purchases | 49996 | 52541 | 55100 |
| Wages | 12800 | 12360 | 14500 |
| Expenses | 8050 | 7450 | 10100 |
| New machine | 13375 | 13375 | 13375 |
| **Total payments** | 85221 | 86333 | 93075 |

**Task 1.6**

The cash budget for Whitesands Industries for the three months ended June has been partially completed. The following information is to be incorporated and the cash budget completed.

■ A bank loan of £75,000 has been negotiated and this will be paid into the business bank account in April.

■ The principal (capital) element of the bank loan (£75,000) is to be repaid in 60 equal monthly installments beginning in May.

■ The loan attracts 8% interest per annum calculated on the amount of the loan principal advanced in April. The annual interest charge is to be paid in equal monthly installments beginning in May.

■ When Whitesands Industries uses its bank overdraft facility interest is payable monthly and is estimated at 2% of the previous months overdraft balance. The interest is to be rounded to the nearest £.

■ At 1 April the balance of the bank account was overdrawn £1,350.

Using the additional information above, complete the cash budget for Whitesands Industries for the three months ending June. Cash inflows should be entered as positive figures and cash outflows as negative figures. Zeroes must be entered where appropriate to achieve full marks.

| | April £ | May £ | June £ |
|---|---|---|---|
| **RECEIPTS** | | | |
| | | | |
| Cash sales | 18,800 | 19,180 | 20,480 |
| Credit sales | 43,085 | 43,520 | 54,852 |
| Bank loan | 75 000 | 0 | 0 |
| | | | |
| **Total receipts** | 136 885 | 62700 | 75 332 |
| | | | |
| **PAYMENTS** | | | |
| | | | |
| Purchases | -46,650 | -47,005 | -42,075 |
| Wages | -18,800 | -18,950 | -18,450 |
| Expenses | -10,350 | -11,260 | -13,260 |
| Capital expenditure | 0 | -79,500 | 0 |
| Bank loan capital repayment | 0 | -1250 | -1250 |
| Bank loan interest | 0 | 500 | -1000 |
| Overdraft interest | 0 | 0 | -667 |
| | | | |
| **Total payments** | 75800 | 158 465 | 76 202 |
| | | | |
| Net cash flow | 61085 | -95765 | -870 |
| Opening bank balance | 1350 | 62435 | -33330 |
| | | | |
| **Closing bank balance** | 62435 | -33330 | -34 200 |

## SECTION 2

### Task 2.1

A cash budget has been prepared for Princewood Ltd for the next five periods.

The budget was prepared based on the following sales volumes and a selling price of £4 per item.

|  | Period 1 | Period 2 | Period 3 | Period 4 | Period 5 |
|---|---|---|---|---|---|
| Sales volume (items) | 8,900 | 9,800 | 9,500 | 8,500 | 9,600 |

The pattern of cash receipts used in the budget assumed 50% of sales were received in the month of sale and the remaining 50% in the month following sale.

In the light of current economic trends Princewood Ltd needs to adjust its cash budget to take account of the following:

■    The selling price from period 1 will be reduced by 5% per item.

■    The pattern of sales receipts changes to 20% of sales received in the month of sale, 60% in the month following sale and the remaining 20% two months after sale.

(a)    Use the table below to calculate the effect of the changes in the forecast amounts and timing of cash receipts for periods 3, 4 and 5:

|  | Period 1 (£) | Period 2 (£) | Period 3 (£) | Period 4 (£) | Period 5 (£) |
|---|---|---|---|---|---|
| Original value of forecast sales | 35,600 | 39,200 | 38,000 | 34,000 | 38,400 |
|  |  |  |  |  |  |
| Original timing of receipts |  |  | 38,600 | 36,000 | 36,200 |
| Revised value of forecast sales | 33 820 | 37240 | 36100 | 32300 | 36480 |
|  |  |  |  |  |  |
| Revised timing of receipts |  |  | 6764 + 22344 7220 36328 | 7448 + 21 660 6460 35568 | 7220 + 19380 7236 33836 |

### Additional information

The company's suppliers have negotiated reduced payment terms with Princewood Limited in return for fixing prices in the medium term. The original budget was prepared on the basis of paying suppliers in the month following purchase. The revised payment terms allow for settlement of 30% in the month of purchase with the remaining 70% payment in the month following purchase. These revised terms come into effect for purchases in period 1.

The original budgeted purchase figures were:

|  | Period 1 *(£)* | Period 2 *(£)* | Period 3 *(£)* | Period 4 *(£)* | Period 5 *(£)* |
|---|---|---|---|---|---|
| Purchases | 21,500 | 21,200 | 20,800 | 22,600 | 23,000 |

30% / 70% 30% / 70% 30% / 70% 30% / 70% / 70% 30%

**(b)** Use the table below to calculate the effect of the changes in the timing of purchase payments for periods 3, 4 and 5:

|  | Period 3 *(£)* | Period 4 *(£)* | Period 5 *(£)* |
|---|---|---|---|
| Original timing of payments | 21200 | 20800 | 22600 |
| Revised timing of payments | 14840 + 6240  21080 | 14560 + 6780  21340 | 15820 + 6900  22720 |

**(c)** Using your calculations from parts (a) and (b), complete the table to show the net effect of the changes to sales receipts and purchase payments for periods 3, 4 and 5.

|  | Period 3 *(£)* | Period 4 *(£)* | Period 5 *(£)* |
|---|---|---|---|
| Changes in sales receipts | +2272 | 432 | 2304 |
| Changes in purchase payments | 120 | -540 | 120 |
| Net change | 2152 | 972 | 2424 |

**Task 2.2**

The quarterly budgeted and actual figures for an organisation are provided below:

|  | Budgeted | Actual |
|---|---|---|
|  | £ | £ |
| Receipts from credit customers | 88,300 | 83,440 |
| Cash sales | 20,130 | 25,110 |
| Payments to credit suppliers | (55,410) | (56,150) |
| Cash purchases | (8,960) | (7,450) |
| Capital expenditure | - | (23,500) |
| Wages and salaries | (17,450) | (18,300) |
| General expenses | (10,900) | (11,464) |
| Net cash flow | 15,710 | (8,314) |
| Opening bank balance | 3,200 | 3,200 |
| Closing bank balance | 18,910 | (5,114) |

(a) Prepare a reconciliation of budgeted cash flow with actual cash flow for the quarter. Select the appropriate description for each entry, and show + or − signs to denote increased or reduced cash. Ensure that the reconciliation balances.

|  | £ |
|---|---|
| Budgeted closing bank balance | 18910 |
| Surplus/Shortfall in receipts from credit customers | −4860 |
| Surplus/Shortfall in cash sales | +4980 |
| Increase/Decrease in payments to credit suppliers | −740 |
| Increase/Decrease in cash purchases | +1510 |
| Increase/Decrease in capital expenditure | −23500 |
| Increase/Decrease in wages and salaries | −850 |
| Increase/Decrease in general expenses | −564 |
| Actual closing bank balance | −5114 |

**(b)** Which one of the following actions, when carried out in isolation, would have avoided the overdrawn bank balance?

✓

| | |
|---|---|
| Received money from credit customers in line with the budget | |
| Generated cash sales in line with the budget | |
| Made payments to credit suppliers in line with the budget | |
| Made any payments for capital expenditure in line with the budget | ✓ |
| Made payments for salaries and wages in line with the budget | |

**(c)** Variances between budget and actual cash flows can occur for a number of reasons. There are also a variety of courses of action available to minimise adverse variances or benefit from favourable variances.

Match each cause of a variance listed on the left with a possible course of action on the right.

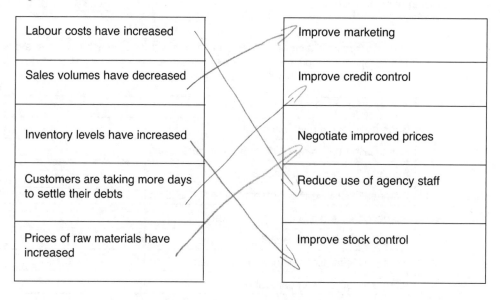

| | |
|---|---|
| Labour costs have increased | Improve marketing |
| Sales volumes have decreased | Improve credit control |
| Inventory levels have increased | Negotiate improved prices |
| Customers are taking more days to settle their debts | Reduce use of agency staff |
| Prices of raw materials have increased | Improve stock control |

**Task 2.3**

**(a)**    A bank overdraft is a common source of finance for businesses. Indicate with a tick the product features which relate to a bank overdraft.

|  | ✔ |
|---|---|
| Interest is calculated on the average annual balance | |
| It is useful for covering working capital requirements | |
| The customer can borrow as much as is required at the time | |
| The account will normally fluctuate from debit (borrowing) to credit (money in the account) | ✓ |

**(b)**    Indicate with a tick the product features which relate to a bank loan.

|  | ✔ |
|---|---|
| Short-term finance, renegotiated annually | |
| Often used for non-current (fixed) asset purchases | ✓ |
| Can be repaid in full at the end of the loan period | |
| Only available at a fixed rate of interest | |

**(c)**    Facility letters are important documents which set out the legal relationship between a bank and a customer that borrows money.

Complete the following sentences using the words listed below.

A facility letter is a document drawn up by the.........*bank*...........and signed by the .....*customer*......in respect of the granting of bank finance. It sets out the .......*default* of the finance and the ......*amount*.....requirements. A facility letter will normally include a ...........*security*.....clause to provide the bank with legal rights and remedies if the customer fails to repay the borrowing.

        **customer**      **default**      **bank**      **security**      **amount**

**Task 2.4**

Mastercraft Limited is a small company which manufactures traditional wooden kitchen furniture. There are four directors.

The company is expanding and requires:

- £100,000 for new production machinery

- additional working capital of £25,000.

The company is profitable and is not borrowing at present but finances its requirements from cashflow.

The directors have now decided that they want to raise finance from the bank to provide £100,000 to finance production machinery and a £25,000 overdraft to cover the increased working capital requirement.

The bank discusses the requirements with the directors and offers the directors of Mastercraft Limited two alternative methods of financing:

**Option 1**

A five year business loan of £100,000 with equal annual repayments, paid at the end of each year. The interest rate is fixed at 6% for the five years and interest is charged annually, calculated on the loan amount outstanding at the time of the repayment.

An arrangement fee of 1.25% is payable at the time the loan is made by the bank to the customer.

The bank is also offering an overdraft facility of £25,000 at an annual rate of 7%. The cash flow forecast estimates that the overdraft for the first year will be at an average level of £15,000. The arrangement fee will be 1.5% of the overdraft limit.

The bank suggests that the directors give their personal guarantees as security, backed by mortgages over their own freehold properties.

**Option 2**

A 'repayment holiday' business loan of £125,000 to cover both the cost of the expansion and also the working capital requirement. An overdraft will therefore not be required.

The loan will be repaid over six years in five equal annual repayments paid at the end of each year, starting at the end of Year 2.

The interest rate will be bank base rate plus 5%. For the first two years, bank base rate is forecast to average 1% and then rise to an average 2% over the last four years.

An arrangement fee of 2% of the whole loan amount is payable at the time the loan is made by the bank to the customer.

The security requested is a fixed and floating charge over the company assets, including premises, machinery, inventory and receivables.

**You are to**

(a)    Calculate the cost of the finance (interest and fees) for each option for the first year, setting out your findings in the following table:

|  | loan interest<br>£ | arrangement fees<br>£ | overdraft interest<br>£ | total cost<br>£ |
|---|---|---|---|---|
| **Option 1** | 6000 | 1250 | 2125 | 9375 |
| **Option 2** | 7500 | 2500 | 0 | 10200 |

(b)    Indicate which option the directors should choose on the basis of the total first year cost of the finance.    ✔

| Option 1 | ✔ |
|---|---|
| Option 2 |  |

(c)    Indicate which option the directors should choose on the basis of the security requirements of the bank.    ✔

| Option 1 |  |
|---|---|
| Option 2 | ✔ |

(d)    The choice of the 'repayment holiday' loan in Option 2 will affect the cash flow of the company in the first year in various ways. Select all the correct options.    ✔

| The amount due in interest payments will be higher | ✔ |
|---|---|
| The amount due in interest payments will be lower. |  |
| The amount due in capital repayment of the loan will be higher | ✔ |
| The amount due in capital repayment of the loan will be lower |  |

**Task 2.5**

Complete the gaps in the text below with the correct word taken from the following:

**low-risk     Treasury Bill     Gilts     high-risk     short-term**

The ............*Gilts*.... market provides long term funding for the UK Government. This is a relatively

...........*low risk*........investment. Another way of providing funding for the UK Government is

investing in the ......*Treasure Bill*...market. This is a ......*short term*.... form of investment.

Investment in company shares on the Stock Market can be relatively ......*high risk*.... and

should only be seen as a long-term investment.

**Task 2.6**

Motrix plc is a large company which distributes parts and accessories for the motor trade on a national basis.

The company runs a Treasury as part of its Finance Department. It has a strict investment policy established in a set of Policies and Procedures. These establish the authorities and responsibilities given to its Treasury employees and  the types of investment which are permissible.

The investment manual of the Treasury includes the following policy for investing short-term surplus funds:

---

- The risk level must be low.

- The investment must be convertible to cash within 60 days.

- The maximum amount to be invested in any one type of investment is £200,000.

- The interest rate must be at least 1.5% above bank base rate.

- No deposits should be placed with financial institutions outside the UK.

---

The Treasury is reviewing its investment options at the beginning of the month and has selected four options for £200,000 which it has immediately available for an investment over one month. Bank base rate is currently 1%.

**Option 1 - Blackstone Technology Fund**

The financial press is recommending investment in this managed fund which is based largely on international technology companies. The fund is currently yielding 5.6% p.a. and offers a potentially high level of growth over the long term. The publicity material sent out by Blackstone contains the sentence suggesting a high level of risk: 'The value of these investments may fall as well as rise.' There is no upper limit on investment in the fund. Minimum investment is £1,000.

**Option 2 – Mercia Bank plc money market account**

This is a UK bank money market based low risk product. The minimum investment allowed is £100,000.  There is no upper limit on investment. There is a choice of two accounts:

- a 'call account' (money can be withdrawn at any time) – interest at 2.125% p.a.

- a one month fixed deposit – interest 2.5% p.a.

**Option 3 – National Bank one year bond**

Investment in a reputable UK bank (low risk) projected interest rate is 4% and a minimum investment of £500,000 is required; one year fixed period.

### Option 4 – RWF Eurobank currency deposit

RWF Eurobank is offering good rates on Euro deposits, including a six month deposit paying 4% on amounts of €100,000 (approximately £85,000) or more. The risk of this investment is low.

**(a)** Complete the table below for each of the four options, writing 'yes' if the investment meets County Treasury policy requirements and 'no' if it does not.

|  | Convertible within 60 days (yes/no) | Available for £250,000 (yes/no) | Interest rate 1% over base (yes/no) | Overseas investment (yes/no) | Level of risk acceptable (yes/no) |
|---|---|---|---|---|---|
| Option 1 | No | Yes | Yes | Yes | No |
| Option 2 | Yes | Yes | Yes | No | Yes |
| Option 3 | No | No | Yes | No | Yes |
| Option 4 | Yes | Yes | Yes | Yes | Yes |

**(b)** State which of the four options should be chosen for the £200,000 available for investment.

|  | ✔ |
|---|---|
| Option 1 - Blackstone Technology Fund |  |
| Option 2 – Mercia Bank plc money market account |  |
| Option 3 – National Bank one year bond |  |
| Option 4 – RWF Eurobank currency deposit | ✓ |

# Cash management

# Practice assessment 2

This Assessment is based on a sample assessment provided by the AAT and is reproduced here with their kind permission.

In view of AAT's intention to introduce International Accounting Standards (IAS) terminology into all its assessments, dual terminology has been introduced by the publisher into this practice assessment. Relevant accounting terminology is quoted in an IAS (UK) format, for example – 'inventory (stock)' and 'payables (creditors)'.

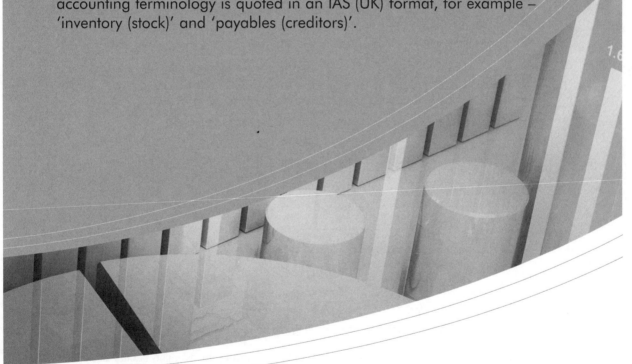

## SECTION 1

**Task 1.1**

**(a)** Complete the diagram below of the working capital cycle by placing the options into the correct boxes.

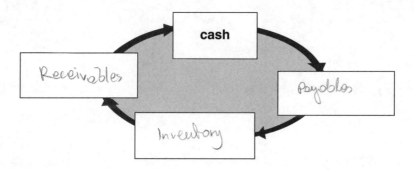

**Options:**

- Payables (creditors)
- Receivables (debtors)
- Inventory (stock)

**(b)** A business has an average inventory (stock) holding period of 94 days, receives payment from its customers in 58 days and pays its payables (creditors) in 75 days.

What is the cash operating cycle in days for the business? (Select one).

✓

| 111 days | |
|----------|---|
| 39 days | |
| 77 days | ✓ |
| 227 days | |

**(c)** Complete the following sentences by selecting the correct options:

Over-trading can occur when a business has **[too much/insufficient]** working capital and over-capitalisation can occur when a business has **[too much/insufficient]** working capital.

Signs of over-trading include **[slowly decreasing/rapidly decreasing/slowly increasing/rapidly increasing]** sales volumes, **[reducing/increasing]** profit margins, **[shorter/longer]** receivable (debtor) collection periods, **[shorter/longer]** payable (creditor) payment periods.

**Task 1.2**

**(a)**    Cash receipts and payments take many different forms but they can be broadly categorised into regular, capital, exceptional and drawings.

Complete the table by selecting the correct description from the list of options below to match the type of cash receipt or cash payment.

| Type of receipt or payment | Description |
|---|---|
| Capital payments | |
| Regular revenue receipts | |
| Drawings | Payments made to the owners of the business |
| Exceptional payments | |

**Options:**

- Payments that relate to the proceeds from the disposal of non-current (fixed) assets

- Payments that relate to the acquisition of non-current (fixed) assets

- Payments made to the owners of the business

- Payments received from the owners of the business

- Income received from HM Revenue & Customs

- Income received from the operating activities of the business that are expected to occur frequently

- Income received from the operating activities of the business that are not expected to occur frequently

- Payments arising from the operating activities of the business that are expected to occur frequently

- Payments arising from the operating activities of the business that are not expected to occur frequently

- Payments that do not arise from the operating activities of the business but that are expected to occur frequently

- Payments that do not arise from the operating activities of the business and that are not expected to occur frequently

**(b)** J Wynn owns an office cleaning business and prepares quarterly income statements (profit and loss accounts) and statements of financial position (balance sheets). These are prepared on an accruals basis.

Cleaning materials are purchased when required and therefore very little inventory (stock) is maintained. All sales and purchases are made on credit terms.

The income statement for J Wynn's business for the quarter ended December is as follows:

|  | £ | £ |
|---|---|---|
| Sales |  | 182,400 |
| Less: Purchases |  | (27,360) |
| Gross profit |  | 155,040 |
| Less: Expenses |  |  |
| Wages | 72,900 |  |
| Rent of office | 12,650 |  |
| Office expenses | 18,640 |  |
| Van expenses | 24,118 |  |
| Van depreciation | 4,190 |  |
|  |  | 132,498 |
|  |  | 22,542 |

Extracts from the statements of financial position at 1 October and 31 December show the following:

| Statement of financial position at: | 1 October | 31 December |
|---|---|---|
|  | £ | £ |
| Receivables (debtors) | 21,620 | 16,400 |
| Payables (creditors) | 760 | 1,124 |
| Accruals – office expenses | 119 | 241 |
| Prepayments – van expenses | 483 | 567 |
| Prepayments – rent of office | 1,200 | 1,450 |

Calculate the actual business cash receipts and cash payments for the quarter to 31 December.

| | £ |
|---|---|
| Sales receipts | 187 620 |
| Purchases payments | 26996 |
| Wages paid | 72900 |
| Rent paid | 12900 |
| Office expenses | 18518 |
| Van expenses | 24202 |
| Van depreciation | 4188 |

**Task 1.3**

A company is preparing its forecast sales and purchase information for January of next year.

The sales volume trend is to be identified using a 3-point moving average based on the actual monthly sales volumes for the current year.

**(a)** Complete the table below to calculate the monthly sales volume trend and identify any monthly variations.

| | Sales volume (units) | Trend | Monthly variation (volume less trend) |
|---|---|---|---|
| August | 9,360 | | |
| | | | |
| September | 5,940 | 6840 | −900 |
| | | | |
| October | 5,220 | 7020 | −1800 |
| | | | |
| November | 9,900 | 7200 | 2700 |
| | | | |
| December | 6,480 | 7380 | |

The monthly sales volume trend is | 180 | units.

**Additional information**

The selling price per unit has been set at £8.

The seasonal variations operate on a 3 month repeating cycle.

Monthly purchases are estimated to be 40% of the value of the forecast sales.

**(b)** Using the trend and the monthly variations identified in part (a), complete the table below to forecast the sales volume, sales value and purchase value for January of the next financial year.

| | Forecast trend | Variation | Forecast sales volume | Forecast sales £ | Forecast purchases £ |
|---|---|---|---|---|---|
| January | 7560 | −1800 | 5760 | 46080 | 18432 |

**Additional information**

The company uses an industry wage rate index to forecast future monthly wage costs. Employees receive a pay increase in March each year. The current monthly wage cost of £6,220 was calculated when the wage index was 163. The forecast wage rate index for the next three months is:

| January | 179 |
| February | 186 |
| March | 193 |

**(c)** If the company uses the forecast wage rate index, what will the wage cost for March be, to the nearest £? (Select one)    ✓

| £7,365 | ✓ |
|--------|---|
| £5,253 | |
| £6,454 | |
| £5,994 | |

## Task 1.4

Sargent Enterprises has been trading for a number of years. The business has requested assistance with calculating sales receipts for entry into a cash budget.

Actual sales values achieved are available for January and February and forecast sales values have been produced for March to June.

Sargent Enterprises estimates that cash sales account for 12% of the total sales. The remaining 88% of sales are made on a credit basis.

**(a)** Complete the table below to show the split of total sales between cash sales and credit sales.

| | Actual | | Forecast | | | |
|---|---|---|---|---|---|---|
| | January | February | March | April | May | June |
| Total sales | 37,500 | 42,000 | 45,000 | 51,000 | 58,000 | 63,750 |
| | | | | | | |
| Cash sales | 4500 | 5040 | 5400 | 6120 | 6960 | 7650 |
| | | | | | | |
| Credit sales | 33000 | 36960 | 39600 | 44880 | 51040 | 56100 |

Sargent Enterprises estimates that 60% of credit sales are received in the month after sale with the balance being received two months after sale. For example, 60% of January's credit sales are received in February with the balance being received in March.

**(b)** Using the table below and your figures from part (a), calculate the timing of sales receipts that would be included in a cash budget for Sargent Enterprises for the period March to June.

|  | Credit sales £ | CASH RECEIVED | | | | |
|---|---|---|---|---|---|---|
|  |  | February £ | March £ | April £ | May £ | June £ |
| January | 33 000 | | 19 800 | 13 200 | | | |
| February | 36 960 | | | 22 176 | 14 784 | | |
| March | 39 600 | | | | 23 760 | 15 840 | |
| April | 44 880 | | | | | 26 928 | 17 952 |
| May | 51 040 | | | | | | 30 624 |
| **Monthly credit sales receipts** | | | 35 376 | 38 544 | 42 768 | 48 576 |

**Task 1.5**

Fortnum Ltd is preparing cash payment figures ready for inclusion in a cash budget. The following information is relevant to the payment patterns for purchases, wages and expenses.

■    Purchases are calculated as 55% of the next month's forecast sales and are paid two months after the date of purchase. For example, purchases in July are based on the estimated sales for August and paid for in September.

| | Actual | | | Forecast | | |
|---|---|---|---|---|---|---|
| | **July** | **August** | **September** | **October** | **November** | **December** |
| | £ | £ | £ | £ | £ | £ |
| Total sales | 84,000 | 86,700 | 85,300 | 89,000 | 90,600 | 91,200 |

■    Wages are paid in the month that they are incurred and expenses are paid in the month after they are incurred. The actual and forecast figures for wages and expenses are:

| | Actual | | | Forecast | | |
|---|---|---|---|---|---|---|
| | **July** | **August** | **September** | **October** | **November** | **December** |
| | £ | £ | £ | £ | £ | £ |
| Wages | 11,750 | 11,750 | 12,000 | 12,300 | 12,300 | 12,750 |
| Expenses (excluding depreciation) | 5,808 | 6,879 | 7,470 | 8,836 | 7,652 | 7,478 |

■    A new machine is to be purchased in October at a total cost of £45,000. Payment for the machine is to be made in three equal monthly instalments, beginning in October.

■    The machine is to be depreciated monthly on a straight-line basis at 20% per annum.

Prepare an extract of the payments section of the cash budget for Fortnum Ltd for the three months ended December.

| | October £ | November £ | December £ |
|---|---|---|---|
| **PAYMENTS** | | | |
| Purchases | 46915 | 48950 | 49830 |
| Wages | 12300 | 12300 | 12750 |
| Expenses | 7470 | 8836 | 7652 |
| New machine | 15000 | 15000 | 15000 |
| **Total payments** | 81685 | 85086 | 85232 |

**Task 1.6**

The cash budget for Goran Industries for the three months ended June has been partially completed. The following information is to be incorporated and the cash budget completed.

■ A bank loan of £43,200 has been negotiated and this will be paid into the business bank account in April.

■ The principal (capital) element of the bank loan (£43,200) is to be repaid in 48 equal monthly instalments beginning in May.

■ The loan attracts 5% interest per annum calculated on the amount of the loan principal advanced in April. The annual interest charge is to be paid in equal monthly instalments beginning in May.

■ When Goran Industries uses its bank overdraft facility interest is payable monthly and is estimated at 1% of the previous month's overdraft balance. The interest is to be rounded to the nearest £.

■ At 1 April the balance of the bank account was £4,232.

Using the additional information above, complete the cash budget for Goran Industries for the three months ending June. Cash inflows should be entered as positive figures and cash outflows as negative figures. Zeroes must be entered where appropriate to achieve full marks.

| | April £ | May £ | June £ |
|---|---|---|---|
| **RECEIPTS** | | | |
| | | | |
| Cash sales | 8,100 | 9,180 | 10,440 |
| Credit sales | 53,064 | 53,516 | 64,152 |
| Bank loan | 43200 | 0 | 0 |
| | | | |
| **Total receipts** | 104364 | 62696 | 74592 |
| | | | |
| **PAYMENTS** | | | |
| | | | |
| Purchases | -34,650 | -37,125 | -42,075 |
| Wages | -18,000 | -18,450 | -18,450 |
| Expenses | -10,318 | -11,269 | -13,254 |
| Capital expenditure | 0 | -49,500 | 0 |
| Bank loan capital repayment | 0 | 900 | 900 |
| Bank loan interest | 0 | 180 | 180 |
| Overdraft interest | 0 | 42 | 176 |
| | | | |
| **Total payments** | 62968 | 117424 | 75035 |
| | | | |
| Net cash flow | 41,396 | -54728 | -443 |
| Opening bank balance | -4232 | 37164 | -17564 |
| | | | |
| **Closing bank balance** | 37164 | -17564 | -18007 |

**Task 2.1**

A cash budget has been prepared for Inzyz Ltd for the next five periods.

The budget was prepared based on the following sales volumes and a selling price of £24 per item.

| | Period 1 | Period 2 | Period 3 | Period 4 | Period 5 |
|---|---|---|---|---|---|
| Sales volume (items) | 1,150 | 1,200 | 1,230 | 1,260 | 1,300 |

The pattern of cash receipts used in the budget assumed 50% of sales were received in the month of sale and the remaining 50% in the month following sale.

In the light of current economic trends Inzyz Ltd needs to adjust its cash budget to take account of the following:

■   The selling price from period 1 will be reduced by 15% per item.

■   The pattern of sales receipts changes to 25% of sales received in the month of sale, 50% in the month following sale and the remaining 25% two months after sale.

**(a)**   Use the table below to calculate the effect of the changes in the forecast amounts and timing of cash receipts for periods 3, 4 and 5:

*20.40*

| | Period 1 (£) | Period 2 (£) | Period 3 (£) | Period 4 (£) | Period 5 (£) |
|---|---|---|---|---|---|
| Original value of forecast sales | 27,600 | 28,800 | 29,520 | 30,240 | 31,200 |
| | | | | | |
| Original timing of receipts | | | 29,160 | 29,880 | 30,720 |
| Revised value of forecast sales | *23 460* | *24 480* | *25092* | *25704* | *26 520* |
| | | | | | |
| Revised timing of receipts | | | *5885+ 12240* *6273* *24378* | *6120+ 12546* *6426* *25032* | *6273+ 12852* *6630* *25755* |

**Additional information**

The company has managed to negotiate extended payment terms with its suppliers. The original budget was prepared on the basis of paying suppliers in the month following purchase. The revised payment terms allow for settlement of 30% in the month following purchase with the remaining payment two months after purchase.

The original budgeted purchase figures were:

|  | Period 1 *(£)* | Period 2 *(£)* | Period 3 *(£)* | Period 4 *(£)* | Period 5 *(£)* |
|---|---|---|---|---|---|
| Purchases | 8,480 | 9,600 | 9,820 | 10,940 | 11,110 |

**(b)** Use the table below to calculate the effect of the changes in the timing of purchase payments for periods 3, 4 and 5:

|  | Period 3 *(£)* | Period 4 *(£)* | Period 5 *(£)* |
|---|---|---|---|
| Original timing of payments | 9600 | 9820 | 10940 |
| Revised timing of payments | 2880 + 5936<br>8816 | 6720 + 2946<br>9666 | 6874 + 3282<br>10156 |

**(c)** Using your calculations from parts (a) and (b), complete the table to show the net effect of the changes to sales receipts and purchase payments for periods 3, 4 and 5.

|  | Period 3 *(£)* | Period 4 *(£)* | Period 5 *(£)* |
|---|---|---|---|
| Changes in sales receipts | − 4782 | − 4788 | − 4965 |
| Changes in purchase payments | 784 | 154 | 784 |
| Net change | − 3998 | − 4634 | − 4181 |

**Task 2.2**

The quarterly budgeted and actual figures for an organisation are provided below:

|  | Budgeted | Actual |
|---|---|---|
|  | £ | £ |
| Receipts from receivables (debtors) | 86,423 | 81,667 |
| Cash sales | 14,350 | 11,780 |
| Payments to payables (creditors) | (42,618) | (44,791) |
| Cash purchases | (7,600) | (7,940) |
| Capital expenditure | - | (28,000) |
| Wages and salaries | (19,200) | (17,600) |
| General expenses | (24,650) | (22,464) |
| Net cash flow | 6,705 | (27,348) |
| Opening bank balance | 4,200 | 4,200 |
| Closing bank balance | 10,905 | (23,148) |

(a) Prepare a reconciliation of budgeted cash flow with actual cash flow for the quarter. Select the appropriate description for each entry.

|  | £ |
|---|---|
| Budgeted closing bank balance | 10905 |
| Surplus/Shortfall in receipts from receivables (debtors) | – 4756 |
| Surplus/Shortfall in cash sales | –2570 |
| Increase/Decrease in payments to payables (creditors) | – 2173 |
| Increase/Decrease in cash purchases | – 340 |
| Increase/Decrease in capital expenditure | – 28 000 |
| Increase/Decrease in wages and salaries | 1600 |
| Increase/Decrease in general expenses | 2186 |
| Actual closing bank balance | – 23 148 |

**(b)**     Which actions (taken in isolation) would have avoided an overdrawn bank balance?

|  | ✓ |
|---|---|
| (a)   Chased customers to pay sooner and delayed payments to payables (creditors) | ✓ |
| (b)   Increased cash sales through better marketing |  |
| (c)   Delayed capital expenditure |  |
| (d)   Negotiated lower wages payments to employees |  |

**(c)**     Variances between budget and actual cash flows can occur for a number of reasons. There are also a variety of courses of action available to minimise adverse variances or benefit from favourable variances.

Match each cause of a variance listed on the left with a possible course of action on the right.

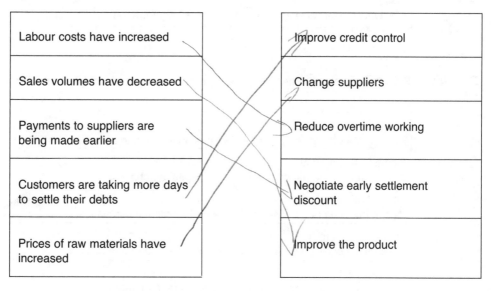

**Task 2.3**

(a)    Which of the following best describes the main features of an overdraft? (Tick one)

|  | ✓ |
|---|---|
| Interest rates are low; it is available for as long as required; it is useful for capital purchases. |  |
| Interest rates are low; it is payable on demand; it is useful for capital purchases. |  |
| Interest rates are low; repayments can be negotiated; it is useful for capital purchases. |  |
| Interest rates are high; repayments can be negotiated; it is a short-term form of finance. |  |
| Interest rates are high; it is repayable on demand; it is a short-term form of finance. | ✓ |
| Interest rates are high; it is available for as long as required; it is a long-term form of finance. |  |

(b)    Which of the following best describes the main features of a bank loan? (Tick one)

|  | ✓ |
|---|---|
| Interest rates are low; it is available for as long as required; it is useful for capital purchases. |  |
| Interest rates are low; it is payable on demand; it is useful for capital purchases. |  |
| Interest rates are low; repayments can be negotiated; it is useful for capital purchases. | ✓ |
| Interest rates are high; repayments can be negotiated; it is a short-term form of finance. |  |
| Interest rates are high; it is repayable on demand; it is a short-term form of finance. |  |
| Interest rates are high; it is available for as long as required; it is a long-term form of finance. |  |

(c)    Complete the sentences below by picking the correct options.

A bank facility letter sets out the **[draft/ possible/ legal/ illegal]** rights and duties of **[the bank/ the customer/ the bank and the customer]** when the bank grants **[an overdraft facility/ a bank loan/ overdrafts and loans]**.

The purpose of a facility letter is to protect the rights of **[the bank/ the customer/ the bank and the customer]**.

**Task 2.4**

The three partner firm of Parry & Associates is planning to expand its production facilities. The expansion plans will require the purchase of new machinery at a cost of £78,000 and a working capital injection of £18,000.

The partnership has been seeking possible means of funding the expansion and has been offered three options:

**Option 1**

A bank loan of £78,000 secured on the new machinery. Capital repayments are to be made over four years in equal instalments. The interest rate is fixed at 6% per annum calculated on the capital balance outstanding at the beginning of each year.

An arrangement fee equal to 1% of the bank loan is payable at the beginning of the loan term.

The bank is also offering an overdraft facility of £19,500 which attracts an annual interest rate of 12%. The partners believe that they will require an average overdraft of £16,000 for eight months of the first year.

**Option 2**

A bank loan of £96,000 secured on the assets of the partnership. Principal (capital) repayments are to be made over four years, with a four month payment holiday at the beginning of the loan term. (This means that repayments of the principal will not begin until the fifth month after the loan is received by the partnership.)

The interest rate is fixed at 6.5% per annum for the first two years and will then revert to a variable interest rate set at 3% above the base rate.

An arrangement fee equal to 0.75% of the bank loan is payable at the beginning of the loan term.

Under this option there will be no requirement for a bank overdraft facility.

**Option 3**

Each of the three partners will take out a personal secured loan of £32,000 repayable over five years at an interest rate of 2.5%. These monies will then be loaned to the partnership as increased capital. Interest of 4% per annum is payable by the partnership to the partners.

Under this option there will be no requirement for a bank overdraft facility.

An extract from the partnership policy in respect of raising finance states the following:

- The maximum overdraft facility that the partnership may obtain is £20,000.

- Interest payable by the partnership is to be kept as low as possible.

- Loan finance may be secured on the assets of the partnership.

- The partners should not give personal guarantees or security for loan finance.

(a) Complete the table below to calculate the cost to the partnership for the first year of financing under each of the three options:

| | Loan interest £ | Arrangement fee £ | Overdraft interest £ | Total cost £ |
|---|---|---|---|---|
| Option 1 | 4680 | 780 | 1320 | 7380 |
| Option 2 | 6240 | 720 | 0 | 6960 |
| Option 3 | 3680 | | | 3680 |

(b) Which financing option should the partnership select taking account of the provision of the partnership policy? (Tick one)

| | ✓ |
|---|---|
| Option 1 | |
| Option 2 | |
| Option 3 | ✓ |
| None of the options | |

**Task 2.5**

Select the correct options to complete the following sentences:

Certificates of deposit are certificates issued by **[banks/ companies/ stock exchange/ local authority]** that certify that an amount of money has been deposited and will be repaid at a specific date in the future. They **[can/cannot]** be traded on a market. They are considered to be a **[low risk/high risk]** investment.

Local authority short-term loans are certificates issued by **[banks/ companies/ stock exchange/ local authorities]** and backed by the government.  They **[can/cannot]** be traded on a market. They are considered to be a **[low risk bank loan/high risk bank loan/low risk investment/high risk investment]**.

Government securities are also known as **[gold-edged/ gilt-edged/ gilted]** securities and **[can/cannot]** be traded. Interest rates are **[fixed/variable]** and these types of securities are considered to be **[low risk/ high risk]** because **[they are/are not]** backed by the government.

**Task 2.6**

The investment manual of a treasury department in a large company has the following policy for investing surplus funds:

■    The investment must be convertible to cash within 60 days.

■    The maximum amount to be invested in any one type of investment is £50,000.

■    The interest rate must be at least 2% above base rate which is currently 0.5%.

■    The investment must not include shares.

■    Only low or medium risk investments are to be selected.


Four possible investment options are available:


**Option 1**

Investment of £50,000 required; 90-day notice period; medium risk; investment portfolio includes shares; interest rate is 2.8% per annum.


**Option 2**

Maximum investment is £80,000 and minimum investment is £30,000; 30-day notice period; interest rate is 1.5% above base rate; low risk; does not include investment in shares.


**Option 3**

Investment portfolio comprises stocks and shares; high risk; projected interest rate is 7% and a minimum investment of £40,000 is required; 45-day notice period.


**Option 4**

Low risk; guaranteed return of 3% per annum; no stocks or shares; minimum investment of £52,000; 7-day notice period.

**(a)**    Complete the table below to show which of the policy requirements are met by each of the four options. State 'yes' or 'no' in each box.

|  | Convertible within 60 days | Investment £50,000 or below | Interest rate 2% above base | Investment does not include shares | Risk |
|---|---|---|---|---|---|
| Option 1 | No | Yes | Yes | No | Yes |
| Option 2 | Yes | Yes | No | Yes | Yes |
| Option 3 | Yes | Yes | Yes | No | No |
| Option 4 | Yes | No | Yes | Yes | Yes |

**(b)**    Complete the sentence to recommend which of the options, if any, should be selected.

The company should select **[Option 1/Option 2/Option 3/Option 4/ none of the options]**.

# Cash management

# Practice assessment answers

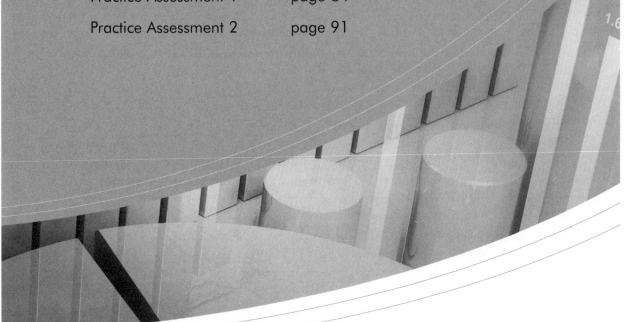

## SECTION 1

**Task 1.1**

(a)

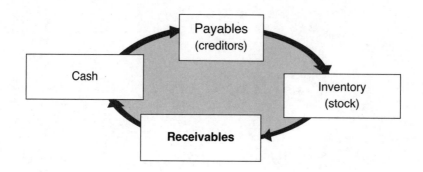

(b) The cash operating cycle in days for the business is

121 days

(c) Over-capitalisation can occur when a business has **too much** working capital and over-trading can occur when a business has **insufficient** working capital.

Signs of over-capitalisation include **high** inventory levels, **high** cash levels, **high** receivables (debtors) levels, and suppliers being paid **early**.

**Task 1.2**

(a)

| Example | Capital payment | Regular revenue payment | Payment for drawings | Exceptional payment |
|---|---|---|---|---|
| Purchase of machinery | ✓ | | | |
| Loan repayments | | ✓ | | |
| Purchase of shares to take over another company | | | | ✓ |
| Final dividends | | | ✓ | |
| Salary payments | | ✓ | | |
| Bank interest payments | | ✓ | | |

**Task 1.2 (b)**

|  | £ | Workings (in £) |
|---|---|---|
| Sales receipts | 103,740 | 103,900 + 680 - 840 |
| Purchases payments | 45,610 | 45,090 + 8,450 – 7,930 |
| Wages paid | 26,430 | No adjustment |
| Rent paid | 8,500 | 9,000 – 1,500 + 1,000 |
| Shop expenses | 5,860 | 5,950 + 120 - 210 |
| Depreciation | 0 | Non cash item |
| Bank interest | 245 | 190 + 55 |
| Drawings | 15,000 | Per narrative |

**Task 1.3**

**(a)**

|  | Sales volume (units) | Trend | Monthly variation (volume less trend) |
|---|---|---|---|
| August | 40,900 |  |  |
| September | 47,300 | 42,300 | +5,000 |
| October | 38,700 | 42,600 | -3,900 |
| November | 41,800 | 42,900 | -1,100 |
| December | 48,200 |  |  |

The monthly sales volume trend is 300 units.

**(b)**

|  | Forecast trend | Variation | Forecast sales volume | Forecast sales £ | Forecast purchases £ |
|---|---|---|---|---|---|
| January | 43,500 | -3,900 | 39,600 | 316,800 | 174,240 |

**(c)**      £24,058

**Task 1.4**

**(a)**

|  | Actual | | Forecast | | | |
|---|---|---|---|---|---|---|
|  | **January** | **February** | **March** | **April** | **May** | **June** |
| Total sales | 48,100 | 49,600 | 49,000 | 52,500 | 51,600 | 49,400 |
| Cash sales | 12,025 | 12,400 | 12,250 | 13,125 | 12,900 | 12,350 |
| Credit sales | 36,075 | 37,200 | 36,750 | 39,375 | 38,700 | 37,050 |

**Task 1.4**

**(b)**

|  | CASH RECEIVED | | | | | |
|---|---|---|---|---|---|---|
|  | **Credit sales** | **February** | **March** | **April** | **May** | **June** |
|  | £ | £ | £ | £ | £ | £ |
| January | 36,075 | 14,430 | 21,645 |  |  |  |
| February | 37,200 |  | 14,880 | 22,320 |  |  |
| March | 36,750 |  |  | 14,700 | 22,050 |  |
| April | 39,375 |  |  |  | 15,750 | 23,625 |
| May | 38,700 |  |  |  |  | 15,480 |
| **Monthly credit sales receipts** |  |  | 36,525 | 37,020 | 37,800 | 39,105 |

**Task 1.5**

|  | October | November | December |
|---|---|---|---|
|  | £ | £ | £ |
| Purchases | 49,996 | 52,548 | 55,100 |
| Wages | 12,800 | 12,960 | 14,500 |
| Expenses | 9,050 | 7,450 | 10,100 |
| New machine | 13,375 | 13,375 | 13,375 |
| **Total payments** | 85,221 | 86,333 | 93,075 |

**Task 1.6**

|  | April £ | May £ | June £ |
|---|---|---|---|
| **RECEIPTS** |  |  |  |
| Cash sales | 18,800 | 19,180 | 20,480 |
| Credit sales | 43,085 | 43,520 | 54,852 |
| Bank loan | 75,000 | 0 | 0 |
| **Total receipts** | 136,885 | 62,700 | 75,332 |
|  |  |  |  |
| **PAYMENTS** |  |  |  |
| Purchases | -46,650 | -47,005 | -42,075 |
| Wages | -18,800 | -18,950 | -18,450 |
| Expenses | -10,350 | -11,260 | -13,260 |
| Capital expenditure | 0 | -79,500 | 0 |
| Bank loan capital repayment | 0 | -1,250 | -1,250 |
| Bank loan interest | 0 | -500 | -500 |
| Overdraft interest | -27 | 0 | -721 |
| **Total payments** | -75,827 | -158,465 | 76,256 |
|  |  |  |  |
| Net cash flow | 61,058 | -95,765 | -924 |
| Opening bank balance | -1,350 | 59,708 | -36,057 |
| **Closing bank balance** | 59,708 | -36,057 | -36,981 |

## SECTION 2

**Task 2.1**

(a)

|  | Period 1 (£) | Period 2 (£) | Period 3 (£) | Period 4 (£) | Period 5 (£) |
|---|---|---|---|---|---|
| Original value of forecast sales | 35,600 | 39,200 | 38,000 | 34,000 | 38,400 |
|  |  |  |  |  |  |
| Original timing of receipts |  |  | 38,600 | 36,000 | 36,200 |
| Revised value of forecast sales | 33,820 | 37,240 | 36,100 | 32,300 | 36,480 |
|  |  |  |  |  |  |
| Revised timing of receipts |  |  | 36,328 | 35,568 | 33,896 |

**Task 2.1**

**(b)**

|  | Period 3 *(£)* | Period 4 *(£)* | Period 5 *(£)* |
|---|---|---|---|
| Original timing of payments | 21,200 | 20,800 | 22,600 |
| Revised timing of payments | 21,080 | 21,340 | 22,720 |

**(c)**

|  | Period 3 *(£)* | Period 4 *(£)* | Period 5 *(£)* |
|---|---|---|---|
| Changes in sales receipts | -2,272 | -432 | -2,304 |
| Changes in purchase payments | +120 | -540 | -120 |
| Net change | -2,152 | -972 | -2,424 |

**Task 2.2   (a)**

|  | £ |
|---|---|
| Budgeted closing bank balance | 18,910 |
| Shortfall in receipts from credit customers | -4,860 |
| Surplus in cash sales | +4,980 |
| Increase in payments to credit  suppliers | -740 |
| Decrease in cash purchases | +1,510 |
| Increase in capital expenditure | -23,500 |
| Increase in wages and salaries | -850 |
| Increase in general expenses | -564 |
| Actual closing bank balance | -5,114 |

**(b)**    Made any payments for capital expenditure in line with the budget

**(c)**

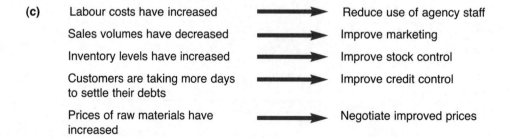

**Task 2.3**

**(a)** It is useful for covering working capital requirements

The account will normally fluctuate from debit (borrowing) to credit (money in the account)

**(b)** Often used for non-current (fixed) asset purchases

Can be repaid in full at the end of the loan period

**(c)** A facility letter is a document drawn up by the **bank** and signed by the **customer** in respect of the granting of bank finance. it sets out the **amount** of the finance and the **security** requirements. Common clauses include a **default** clause to provide the bank with legal rights and remedies if the customer fails to repay the borrowing.

**Task 2.4**

**(a)**

|  | loan interest | arrangement fees | overdraft interest | total cost |
|---|---|---|---|---|
|  | £ | £ | £ | £ |
| **Option 1** | 6,000 | 1,625 | 1,050 | 8,675 |
| **Option 2** | 7,500 | 2,500 | – | 10,000 |

**(b)** Option 1

**(c)** Option 2

**(d)** The amount due in interest payments will be higher

The amount due in capital repayment of the loan will be lower

**Task 2.5** The **Gilts** market provides long term funding for the UK Government. This is a relatively **low risk** investment. Another way of providing funding for the UK Government is investing in the **Treasury Bill** market. This is a **short-term**. form of investment. Investment in company shares on the Stock Market can be relatively **high-risk** and should only be seen as a long-term investment.

**Task 2.6**

(a)

|  | Convertible within 60 days *(yes/no)* | Available for £200,000 *(yes/no)* | Interest rate 1% over base *(yes/no)* | Overseas investment *(yes/no)* | Level of risk acceptable *(yes/no)* |
|---|---|---|---|---|---|
| **Option 1** | yes | yes | yes | no | no |
| **Option 2** | yes | yes | yes | yes | yes |
| **Option 3** | no | no | yes | yes | yes |
| **Option 4** | no | yes | yes | no | yes |

(b)     Option 2 – Mercia Bank plc money market account

# Cash management

# Practice assessment 2
answers

**Section 1**

**Task 1.1**

   **(a)**

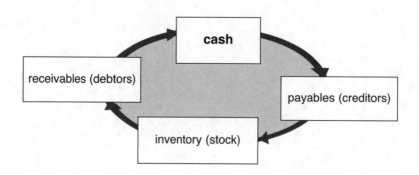

   **(b)**    94 + 58 – 75 = 77 so correct choice is C

               *Note: incorrect answers calculated as:*

               94 – 58 + 75 = 111

               58 + 75 – 94 = 39

               94 + 58 + 75 = 227

   **(c)**    Over-trading can occur when a business has **insufficient** working capital and over-capitalisation can occur when a business has **too much** working capital.

               Signs of over-trading include **rapidly increasing** sales volumes, **reducing** profit margins, **longer** receivable (debtor) collection periods, **longer** payable (creditor) payment periods.

**Task 1.2**

   **(a)**

| Type of receipt or payment | Description |
|---|---|
| Capital payments | Payments that relate to the acquisition of non-current assets (fixed assets) |
| Regular revenue receipts | Income received from the operating activities of the business that are expected to occur frequently |
| Drawings | Payments made to the owners of the business |
| Exceptional payments | Payments that do not arise from the operating activities of the business and that are not expected to occur frequently |

**Task 1.2 (b)**

|  | £ | *Workings* |
|---|---|---|
| Sales receipts | 187,620 | 182,400 + 21,620 – 16,400 |
| Purchases payments | 26,996 | 27,360 + 760 – 1,124 |
| Wages paid | 72,900 | No adjustment |
| Rent paid | 12,900 | 12,650 – 1,200 +1,450 |
| Office expenses | 18,518 | 18,640 + 119 – 241 |
| Van expenses | 24,202 | 24,118 – 483 + 567 |
| Van depreciation | 0 | Non- cash item |

**Task 1.3**

**(a)**

|  | Sales volume (units) | Trend | Monthly variation (volume less trend) |
|---|---|---|---|
| August | 9,360 |  |  |
| September | 5,940 | 6,840 | -900 |
| October | 5,220 | 7,020 | –1,800 |
| November | 9,900 | 7,200 | + 2,700 |
| December | 6,480 |  |  |

The monthly sales volume trend is 180 units.

**(b)**

|  | Forecast trend | Variation | Forecast sales volume | Forecast sales £ | Forecast purchases £ |
|---|---|---|---|---|---|
| January | 7,560 | -1,800 | 5,760 | 46,080 | 18,432 |

**(c)**        £6,220 ÷ 163 x 193 = **7,365**

*Note:*

incorrect answers calculated as:

£6,220 ÷ 193 x 163 = 5,253

£6,220 ÷ 186 x 193 = 6,454

£6,220 ÷ 193 x 186 = 5,994

## Task 1.4

### (a)

|  | Actual | | Forecast | | | |
|---|---|---|---|---|---|---|
|  | January | February | March | April | May | June |
| Total sales | 37,500 | 42,000 | 45,000 | 51,000 | 58,000 | 63,750 |
| Cash sales (12%) | 4,500 | 5,040 | 5,400 | 6,120 | 6,960 | 7,650 |
| Credit sales (88%) | 33,000 | 36,960 | 39,600 | 44,880 | 51,040 | 56,100 |

## Task 1.4

### (b)

| | CASH RECEIVED | | | | | |
|---|---|---|---|---|---|---|
| | Credit sales | February | March | April | May | June |
| | £ | £ | £ | £ | £ | £ |
| January | 33,000 | 19,800 | 13,200 | | | |
| February | 36,960 | | 22,176 | 14,784 | | |
| March | 39,600 | | | 23,760 | 15,840 | |
| April | 44,880 | | | | 26,928 | 17,952 |
| May | 51,040 | | | | | 30,624 |
| Monthly credit sales receipts | | | 35,376 | 38,544 | 42,768 | 48,576 |

## Task 1.5

| | October | November | December |
|---|---|---|---|
| | £ | £ | £ |
| Payments | | | |
| Purchases | 46,915 | 48,950 | 49,830 |
| Wages | 12,300 | 12,300 | 12,750 |
| Expenses | 7,470 | 8,836 | 7,652 |
| New machine | 15,000 | 15,000 | 15,000 |
| Total payments | 81,685 | 85,086 | 85,232 |

**Task 1.6**

|  | April | May | June |
|---|---|---|---|
|  | £ | £ | £ |
| **RECEIPTS** |  |  |  |
| Cash sales | 8,100 | 9,180 | 10,440 |
| Credit sales | 53,064 | 53,516 | 64,152 |
| Bank loan | 43200 | 0 | 0 |
| Total receipts | 104,364 | 62,696 | 74,592 |
|  |  |  |  |
| Payments |  |  |  |
| Purchases | -34,650 | -37,125 | -42,075 |
| Wages | -18,000 | -18,450 | -18,450 |
| Expenses | -10,318 | -11,269 | -13,254 |
| Capital expenditure | 0 | -49,500 | 0 |
| Bank loan capital repayment | 0 | -900 | -900 |
| Bank loan interest | 0 | -180 | -180 |
| Overdraft interest | 0 | 0 | -91 |
| Total payments | -62,968 | -117,424 | -74,950 |
|  |  |  |  |
| Net cash flow | 41,396 | -54,728 | -358 |
| Opening bank balance | 4,232 | 45,628 | -9,100 |
| Closing bank balance | 45,628 | -9,100 | -9,458 |

**Task 2.1**

(a)

|  | Period 1 (£) | Period 2 (£) | Period 3 (£) | Period 4 (£) | Period 5 (£) |
|---|---|---|---|---|---|
| Original value of forecast sales | 27,600 | 28,800 | 29,520 | 30,240 | 31,200 |
|  |  |  |  |  |  |
| Original timing of receipts |  |  | 29,160 | 29,880 | 30,720 |
| Revised value of forecast sales | 23,460 | 24,480 | 25,092 | 25,704 | 26,520 |
|  |  |  |  |  |  |
| Revised timing of receipts |  |  | 24,378 | 25,092 | 25,755 |

**Task 2.1**

**(b)**

|  | Period 3 *(£)* | Period 4 *(£)* | Period 5 *(£)* |
|---|---|---|---|
| Original timing of payments | 9,600 | 9,820 | 10,940 |
| Revised timing of payments | 8,816 | 9,666 | 10,156 |

**(c)**

|  | Period 3 *(£)* | Period 4 *(£)* | Period 5 *(£)* |
|---|---|---|---|
| Changes in sales receipts | -4,782 | -4,788 | -4,965 |
| Changes in purchase payments | 784 | 154 | 784 |
| Net change | -3,998 | -4,634 | -4,181 |

**Task 2.2   (a)**

|  | £ |
|---|---|
| Budgeted closing bank balance | 10,905 |
| Shortfall in receipts from receivables (debtors) | (4,756) |
| Shortfall in cash sales | (2,570) |
| Increase in payments to payables (creditors) | (2,173) |
| Increase in cash purchases | (340) |
| Increase in capital expenditure | (28,000) |
| Decrease in wages and salaries | 1,600 |
| Decrease in general expenses | 2,186 |
| Actual closing bank balance | (23,148) |

**(b)**   (c)  Delayed capital expenditure

(Note: Although the other options could have resulted in a lower overdraft they are not sufficient in and of themselves to reduce the deficit by £23,148)

**(c)**

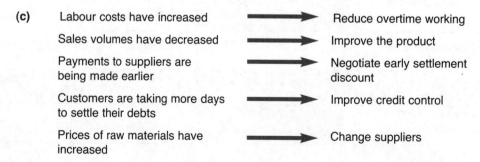

| | |
|---|---|
| Labour costs have increased | Reduce overtime working |
| Sales volumes have decreased | Improve the product |
| Payments to suppliers are being made earlier | Negotiate early settlement discount |
| Customers are taking more days to settle their debts | Improve credit control |
| Prices of raw materials have increased | Change suppliers |

**Task 2.3**

(a)    Interest rates are high; it is repayable on demand; it is a short-term form of finance.

(b)    Interest rates are low; repayments can be negotiated; it is useful for capital purchases.

(c)    A bank facility letter sets out the **legal** rights and duties of **the bank and the customer** when the bank grants **overdrafts and loans**.

The purpose of a facility letter is to protect the rights of **the bank and the customer**.

**Task 2.4**

(a)

|  | Loan interest £ | Arrangement fee £ | Overdraft interest £ | Total cost £ |
|---|---|---|---|---|
| Option 1 | 4,680 | 780 | 1,280 | 6,740 |
| Option 2 | 6,240 | 720 | 0 | 6,960 |
| Option 3 | 3,840 | 0 | 0 | 3,840 |

(b)    Option 1

**Task 2.5**

Certificates of deposit are certificates issued by **banks** that certify that an amount of money has been deposited and will be repaid at a specific date in the future. They **can** be traded on a market. They are considered to be a **low risk** investment.

Local authority short-term loans are certificates issued by **local authorities** and backed by the government. They **can** be traded on a market. They are considered to be a **low risk investment.**

Government securities are also known as **gilt-edged** securities and **can** be traded. Interest rates are **fixed** and these types of securities are considered to be **low risk** because **they are** backed by the government.

**Task 2.6**

(a)

|  | Convertible within 60 days | Investment £50,000 or below | Interest rate 2% above base | Investment does not include shares | Risk |
|---|---|---|---|---|---|
| Option 1 | no | yes | yes | no | yes |
| Option 2 | yes | yes | no | yes | yes |
| Option 3 | yes | yes | yes | no | no |
| Option 4 | yes | no | yes | yes | yes |

(b)    The company should select **none of the options**.

**for your notes**

**for your notes**